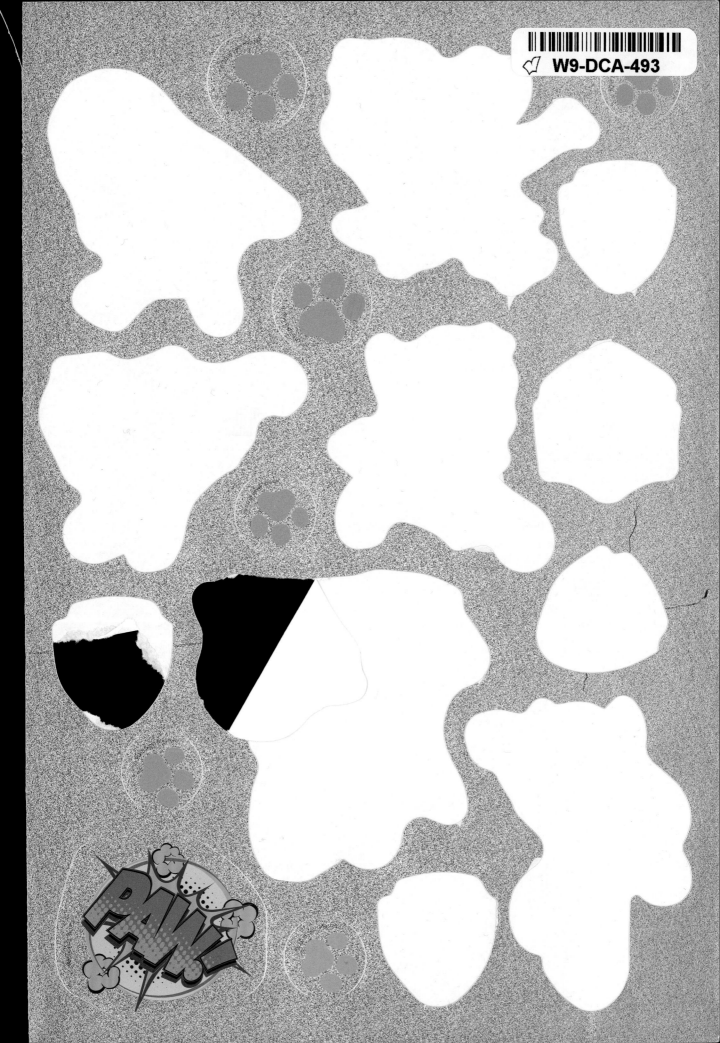

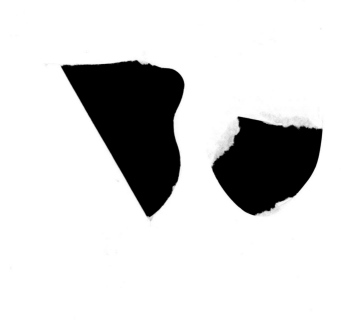

Pages 2-3

© 2018 Spin Master

© 2018 Spin Master

Pages 4-5

© 2018 Spin Master

© 2018 Spin Master

© 2018 Spin Master

© 2018 Spin Master

Pages 8-9

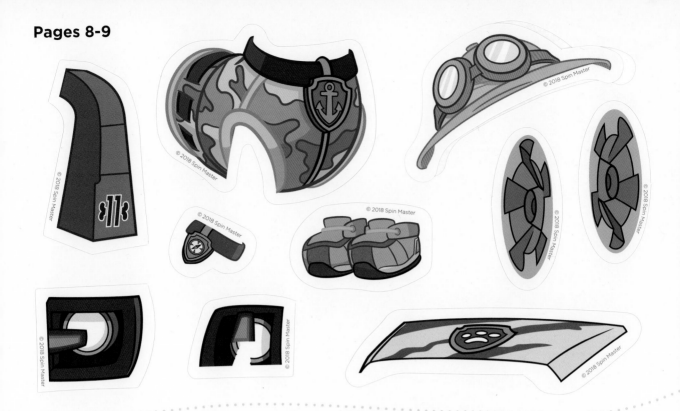

Pages 10-11

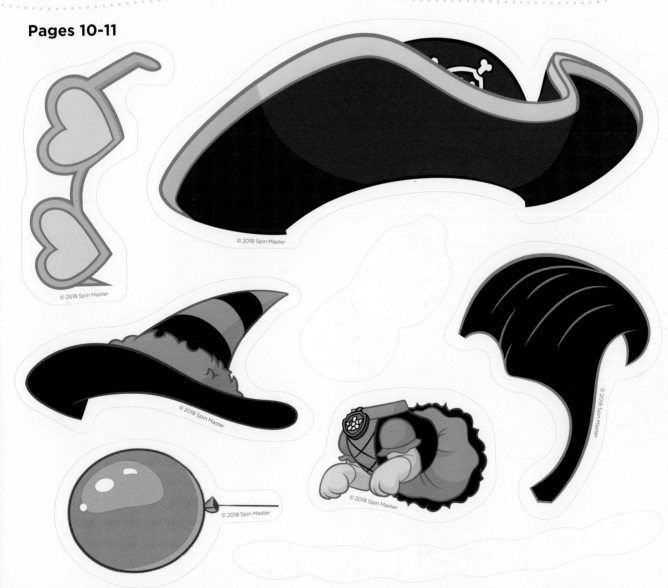

Pages 12-13

Pages 14-15

Pages 16-17

Pages 20-21

Pages 22-23

Page 24

STICKER PUP PLAYTIME

PaRRagon

Bath • New York • Cologne • Melbourne • Delhi
Hong Kong • Shenzhen • Singapore

HERE TO HELP

It's time for a ruff-ruff rescue!
Use your stickers to help
Ryder, Chase and Marshall
get rescue-ready.

03

2

Find the missing stickers to finish the fire engine. Don't forget to add Marshall!

TAKE TO THE SKIES!

Don't forget Rubble's hoverboard propeller!

The pups become heroes of the sky in their amazing flight suits! Help Rubble, Skye and Chase get ready for take-off with your stickers.

Add Chase's boots and jet-powered glider to complete his flight suit.

5

HIT THE SLOPES

Everest zooms down the snowy mountain on her super-fast snowboard. Use your stickers to add trees and penguins to finish this snowy scene.

6

Snow isn't just for snowboarding!
Help Chase and Skye finish their snowman.
Add a hat, nose, scarf and buttons.

© 2018 Spin Master

INTO THE JUNGLE

Can you find Skye's hat, Zuma's uniform and Rocky's shoes?

Skye, Zuma and Rocky are joining their new pal Tracker for a jungle adventure! Go wild with your stickers and get the pups ready to swing to the rescue.

Find the missing stickers to complete Tracker's jungle jeep!

9

DRESSED-UP PUPS

It's not all work and no play for these heroic pals. Use your stickers to dress-up the pups in hats, glasses and wigs for a fancy-dress party!

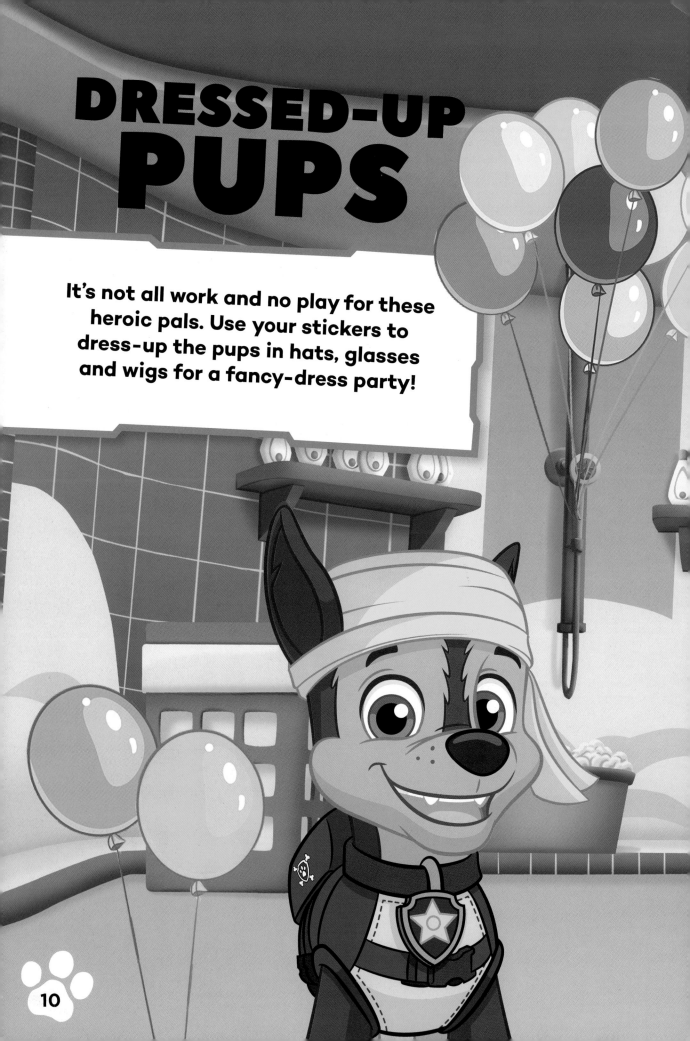

Be silly with your stickers and have fun!

11

PUP HEROES

The PAW Patrol pups have their very own superpower – teamwork! Give these super pups capes and add Rocky's mask.

TIME TO COLOUR

You'll need your crayons and pencils from this page onwards – it's colouring time!

Colour in these super pups, and then use your stickers to add a mask for Skye, and badges for Rubble and Chase.

SURF'S PUP

Help Skye get ready for the beach!
Colour in her beach towel and then use your
stickers to add her collar, sunglasses and hat.

SILLY STYLING

It's playtime for Rocky and Zuma! What game do you think they should play?

Colour in the pups, and then use your stickers to give them crowns, moustaches, wings and more!

15

SEA PATROL

These brave pups are underwater heroes, too! Colour in Skye, Marshall, Rubble and Chase and use your stickers to complete their cool scuba suits.

Find two extra fish on your sticker sheet. Then use your pencils to draw even more!

ADVENTURES IN THE BAY

Zuma and Cap'n Turbot are out on the water in Adventure Bay. Use your stickers and colouring pencils to get them shipshape!

Who's in trouble? Add the creature who needs Zuma's help!

19

LET'S FIX IT!

Rocky is helping Yumi fix a fence on the farm. Which tools will he need? Use your stickers to give Rocky the right tools for the job.

Colour in Yumi's hat, and then add her overalls with your stickers.

20

FARM FRIENDS

Colour in these farm friends, and then use your stickers to give Bettina her cow bell.

ALL STAR PUPS

Ryder and Marshall are missing their headbands!

The PAW Patrol loves working together as a team. Use your stickers and colouring pencils to get Ryder and the pups ready for some active fun in the park.

What game should they play? Find the ball on your sticker sheet, and then add some more active pups!

23

GOOD PUPS

The pups deserve a treat! Colour in the shapes on their bowls and then use your stickers to fill them with snacks.

Pawfriendly
Landscapes™

Lifevest Publishing, Inc.
CENTENNIAL, COLORADO

...ous used in this book have worked for homeowners and
...their pets in our experience, they may not be effective for your backyard Barney.
(Pets can be creative.) We suggest that you also confer with your own landscape
experts.

Also, when installing edging or any other hardscape materials, take extra care to
follow installation instructions specified by the manufacturer.

Pawfriendly Landscapes
is written by Elizabeth Bublitz
Copyright © 2008 Elizabeth Bublitz

Published and Printed by:
  Lifevest Publishing
  4901 E. Dry Creek Rd., #170
  Centennial, CO 80122
  www.lifevestpublishing.com

Printed in the United States of America

I.S.B.N. 1-59879-525-2